This book belongs to...

MELANIN GANG

An ABC Affirmation Book

Written By
Myesha and Mohammed Shuaibe

Illustrated By
Ana Latese

DEDICATED TO THE
YOUNG BLACK KINGS
AND QUEENS OF
THE WORLD.

A

A is for AMAZING. Today will be an amazing day.

B

B is for BELIEVE. I believe in myself and my abilities.

C

C is for CREATE. I have the power to create change.

D

D is for DESERVE. I deserve the best and I accept the best.

E

E is for ENTHUSIASM.
Everything I do, I do with
enthusiasm.

F

**F is for FEARLESS.
There are no challenges I
cannot overcome.**

G

G is for GRATEFUL. I am grateful for everything I am, everything I know, and everything I have.

H

H is for HAPPINESS. My happiness is up to me.

I is for IMAGINATION. My imagination knows no boundaries.

J

J is for JOY. My joy uplifts and empowers me.

K

K is for KIND. I act with kindness.

L

L is for LOVE. I love
and accept myself.

M is for MISTAKES. My mistakes help me learn and grow.

N

N is for NOURISH. I nourish my body with good food and exercise.

O is for OPPORTUNITIES. I am ready to seize the opportunities of the day.

P

P is for POSITIVE. My positive thoughts create positive feelings.

Q is for QUALIFIED.
I am fully equipped and qualified to
achieve great things.

R

R is for RESPECT, because I love myself. Others love and respect me too.

S

S is for STRONG. I am
strong inside and out.

T

T is for THANKFUL. I am thankful for the gift of life.

U

U is for UNIQUE. I love myself and embrace my uniqueness.

V

V is for VISUALIZE. I constantly visualize my purpose, seeing it clearly in my minds eye.

W is for WORTHY.
I am worthy of love, peace, and joy.

X Y Z

What will be
will be.